What Is Red?
¿Qué es rojo?

by Deborah Schecter

ISBN: 978-1-338-70285-9
Illustrated by Anne Kennedy
Copyright © 2020 by Deborah Schecter. All rights reserved.
Published by Scholastic Inc., 557 Broadway, New York, NY 10012

10 9 8 7 6   68   23 24 25 26/0

Printed in Jiaxing, China. First printing, June 2020.

Apples are red.
Red, red, red.

Las manzanas son rojas.
Rojas, rojas, rojas.

Strawberries are red.
Red, red, red.

Las fresas son rojas.
Rojas, rojas, rojas.

Fire trucks are red.
Red, red, red.

Los camiones de bomberos
son rojos.
Rojos, rojos, rojos.

Stop signs are red.
Red, red, red.

Las señales de alto son rojas.
Rojas, rojas, rojas.

Flowers are red.
Red, red, red.

Las flores son rojas.
Rojas, rojas, rojas.

Hearts are red.
Red, red, red.

Los corazones son rojos.
Rojos, rojos, rojos.

My face is red.
Red, red, red!

Me puse rojo.
¡Rojo, rojo, rojo!